Contents

WITHDRAWN

44 0534318 7

NRPB-R291

Doses in Radiation Accidents Investigated
by Chromosome Aberration Analysis
XXI: Review of Cases Investigated, 1994–1996

D C Lloyd, A A Edwards, J E Moquet, P Finnon and P A Hone

Abstract

During the 3 years 1994–1996, 54 persons suspected of being overexposed to ionising radiation were referred to the National Radiological Protection Board for investigation by cytogenetic analysis. Of these, 34 were associated with industrial uses of radiation, 4 were from major nuclear organisations and 16 were from institutions of research, education or health. No evidence of radiation exposure, as indicated by dicentric chromosomal aberrations in blood lymphocytes, was found in 32 persons. In the remainder chromosomal aberration yields were mostly consistent with low doses, 16 being probably in the range 0–100 mGy which is below the statistical limit of reasonable accuracy for the technique. The most serious cases investigated were an approximately whole body exposure estimated to be about 250 mGy, and a localised exposure to hands estimated at ≥ 30 Gy which caused burns. The report contains an appendix in which a brief description is given of the circumstances of each investigation.

National Radiological Protection Board
Chilton
Didcot
Oxon OX11 0RQ

Approval date: November 1996
Publication date: December 1996

Stationery Office, £5.00
ISBN 0 85951 403 X

UNIVERSITY OF HERTFORDSHIRE
HATFIELD CAMPUS LRC
HATFIELD AL10 9AD   342558

BIB
085957403X

CLASS
363.1799 DOS

LOCATION
FWL

BARCODE
44053 43187

1 Introduction

This report is the twenty-first in a series that contains summaries of dosimetry investigations, using chromosomal analysis, undertaken by the National Radiological Protection Board. It covers the 3 years 1994–1996, during which time 54 persons were referred for chromosomal analysis. This brings the total number of cases examined since the cytogenetics laboratory was established in 1968 to 904. In common with previous reports in the series, each of the investigations is briefly described in an appendix comparing, where possible, biological and physical estimates of dose. The biological estimates are expressed in grays and are equivalent uniform whole body doses. They are based on the incidence of dicentric aberrations in chromosomes from circulating T-lymphocytes and are obtained by reference to published *in vitro* dose–response curves. The physical estimates, expressed in sieverts, are usually obtained from film or thermoluminescence personal dosemeters and represent dose equivalent at or near the surface of the body.

During the past 3 years, NRPB has developed the ability to use fluorescence *in situ* hybridisation (FISH) as an alternative method for chromosomal analysis. This may be used as a retrospective dosemeter long (> 1 year) after exposure. *In vitro* dose–response curves for 250 kV x rays, cobalt-60 γ rays and a fission spectrum of neutrons have been prepared. Most cases referred to the laboratory do not involve a long delay before blood sampling and therefore the conventional dicentric analysis would remain the method of choice. Indeed, in the 3 years covered by this report, no case was referred in which it was felt necessary to employ FISH. The technique is still being validated with respect to several important factors such as the long-term persistence of so-called stable translocations, and the effect of non-uniform exposure. As currently applied, it should be possible using FISH and analysing about 5000 cells to achieve a lower limit of whole body dose detection of about 0.2 Gy for x or γ rays.

2 Summary of cases investigated

As in previous reports in this series, brief details of each case investigated during the 3 years are given in an appendix and the numbering system has continued from the 1991–1993 report (NRPB-R268).

Cases have been divided into four categories depending on the reasons for undertaking the investigation. They are shown in Table 1, where the largest category, A, comprising 30 persons, is that where the first indication of a problem is usually a positive reading on a personal physical dosemeter. There is a need to determine whether the recorded dose accurately reflects the true dose, if any, to the wearer. Category B, comprising 18 persons, is that where overexposures were suspected but no physical dosemeter was worn. This is either because the worker neglected to wear a badge or because a non-radiation worker, or possibly even a member of the public, became involved in an incident. In this situation, the chromosomal method may be the only way of deriving a quantitative measurement of dose. There were no cases added to category C, which would include serious overexposures that were sufficiently well defined to permit a detailed reconstruction. The final category, D, comprises 6 persons who were referred for suspected exposure received chronically either due to possible intake of radionuclides or due to long-term unmonitored regular work with external radiation sources. As has been noted in previous reports, the majority of cases (see Table 2) arose from industrial uses of radiation, in particular, γ radiographic sources used for non-destructive testing.

Tables 2 and 3 show that most persons examined had levels of chromosomal damage consistent with a low or zero dose. The terms 'low' and 'zero' used here require further explanation as it should be borne in mind that the biological method does not have the fine level of precision for small doses that can be discriminated by electronic or solid-state personal dosemeters. 'Zero' dose is used to mean that no dicentric aberrations were observed in the sample of cells scored (a minimum of 500); this would carry an upper 95% confidence limit of about 200 mGy for γ radiation. One dicentric observed in 500 cells when converted to dose by reference to *in vitro* calibration curves would indicate 50 mGy of x rays or 100 mGy of γ rays. This assumes that the control level of dicentrics is zero. In reality there is a low background level which in a number of published surveys of control subjects, including data from NRPB, is generally found to be about one dicentric in 1000 cells. Therefore at this level an average person not exposed to radiation, apart from natural background, would be expected to show no dicentrics or one dicentric in 500 cells with equal probability.

When reporting results of chromosomal analyses to physicians, or others, the control incidence of dicentrics is stressed and the opinion given that an indication of exposure in excess of background is only tenable when two or more dicentrics are observed in 500 cells. When no dicentrics are observed, whilst the most likely dose is zero, a better interpretation would be < 100 mGy, this being regarded as the lower practical limit of detection for x or γ rays by the chromosomal method.

Although each case is unique, a number of common threads may be discerned. In some instances investigators came to the conclusion that, whilst the badge had received an overexposure, the wearer probably had not. The absence of chromosomal damage often helped to strengthen a worker's explanation that the badge had been lost or accidentally left in a radiation area. Cases A440, A448, A456, A458 and A463 are examples of this, and, in the instance of case A448, the recorded dose, being so high, was most improbable as the worker was obviously in good health. In other cases (A444, A447, A454, A460 and A464) no explanation could be proffered by the badge holder, nor could investigators find a reason for the recorded overdose. Indeed, for case A460, the man had ceased working with radiation years previously and it was a surprise to the company that they were still issuing him with a dosemeter. When cases such as these are not fully resolved, lingering doubts can lead to concerns and the absence of chromosomal damage often proves reassuring. Unresolved cases can also lead, by default, to a suspicion of deliberate exposure of a person's badge, and, in case A454, there were additional indications that this was the cause.

Cases A446 and A462 are also situations where no clear explanation could be derived, but here chromosomal aberrations were found. In both instances, the view was taken that exposures had occurred. For A446, only one dicentric in 500 cells was observed, which is not significantly different from background (see discussion above). The chromosomal analysis could therefore not resolve the problem. However, it could be concluded that any exposure was low, in terms of the risk of consequences to health, at < 100 mGy, and this was consistent with the 80 mSv recorded by the thermoluminescence dosemeter.

Two cases, A439 and A461, were confounded by the fact that persons had recently received medical irradiations sufficient to cause detectable chromosomal damage. However, fortunately, in each case there was a second person involved with no medical history whose badge dose was not confirmed by the cytogenetics. This, together with other information gleaned by the investigators, led to the conclusion that occupational overexposures had not occurred. Cases A442 and A453 are similar in that there were other work colleagues present, who, had there been a real exposure, would probably also have been irradiated, but their thermoluminescence dosemeters were clear. By contrast, in case A443, there probably was a small exposure to two men which was calculated to be approximately 5 mSv. This is within the worker dose limit, and agreed with the value recorded on one of the thermoluminescence badges. The other dosemeter, however, recorded an inexplicably much larger dose and this could not be confirmed by chromosomal analysis.

2

Cases B109 and B110 each also involved several persons who were, however, not wearing dosemeters. The circumstances of the incidents were such that the persons comprised homogeneous groups with regard to any likely exposure, and so could be considered as 'controls' for each other. This was important in case B109 where one person out of six was found to have an elevated dicentric yield and, as aberration levels in his colleagues were unremarkable, it could be inferred that the dicentrics were unconnected with the incident that prompted the investigation. In the other case, B110, none of the four people involved showed aberration yields significantly different from background. These cases, and, indeed, typically those that are grouped in category B where no dosemeters are worn, may involve persons who are not radiation workers (B109, B110, B111 and B113), hospital patients (B108 and B112) or, in one case, a member of the public (B107) who suspected that a radiation source had been introduced into the home. These people usually have no particular scientific training and only a lay knowledge of radiation hazards. Consequently they are often prone to fear the worst and it is particularly useful and reassuring to be able to demonstrate no or insignificant levels of chromosomal damage in their blood cells. Such fears are, however, not confined to untrained persons. This is illustrated by cases B106 and B115 who were radiation workers involved in an incident and who had failed to wear their dosemeters. Despite firm assurances from professional advisors that their exposure was trivial (B115) or non-existent (B106), they still required the reassurance of a chromosomal examination. Case B106 was interesting in that whilst it was quite clear that no exposure had occurred one highly aberrant cell was found. This was an example of what has been termed a 'rogue' cell and the current view[*] is that these are unrelated to radiation and are probably due to virus infections.

During the 3 years covered by this report, several cases arose for which it was clear that irradiation had occurred, often not disputed by the workers, but the circumstances were such that the doses received could not be reliably evaluated from the accounts given and/or the doses recorded on badges. Cases A441, A450 and B114 are examples where deliberate bypassing of safety procedures occurred, whilst cases A437, A445, A452 and A459 resulted from reliance being placed upon equipment or design which proved to be inadequate. The geometries of non-uniform irradiations were such that the badges could not be relied upon to reflect accurately the doses received. Cases A437 and A449 are instances where the dosemeter was probably closer to the radiation source than much of the wearer's body, whilst A441 and A452 are examples of the opposite situation where the badges were probably outside narrow or collimated beams. Part body exposures confined to the extremities were not registered by chest-worn badges in cases A441 and A438. In the former, an immensely high dose of at least 30 Gy was deduced from the development of rapid dermal ulceration when the hands were placed in an x-ray beam. In the latter it was only by good fortune that a similar dose was avoided when, in a reflex action, a worker briefly picked up a 3.7 TBq (100 Ci) iridium-192 source. In both cases, a few chromosomal aberrations were seen in the blood lymphocytes, but the cytogenetic method is not suited for dose estimation when exposure is confined to such a small volume of the body. Another high extremity exposure was experienced in case A455, but here the worker was correctly wearing a finger-tip dosemeter and it was clear that the irradiation was confined to one hand only.

The most serious overexposures investigated during the 3 year period were, firstly, case A441 where a dose estimated to be at least 30 Gy was confined to the hands and, secondly, case A450 where an average whole body exposure of about 250 mGy was estimated from the chromosomal analysis. Both arose from the deliberate bypassing of safety systems.

---

[*] Neel, J V, *et al.* Hypothesis: 'Rogue cell'-type chromosomal damage in lymphocytes is associated with infection with the JC human polyoma virus and has implications for oncogenesis. *Proc. Natl Acad. Sci. USA*, **93**, 2690–95 (1996).

TABLE 1 Distribution of investigations between the four categories

Category		Previous reports	Present report	Totals
A	Possible non-uniform exposure in which the relationship between dose to the physical dosemeter and to the body is uncertain	547	30	577
B	Suspected overexposure of persons not wearing a dosemeter	180	18	198
C	Overexposure where satisfactory estimates of the whole body dose can be made from physical measurements	7	0	7
D	Chronic internal or external exposure	116	6	122
TOTAL		850	54	904

TABLE 2 Origins of the cases and the number of 'zero' dose estimates

Case origin	Number of cases		Number of 'zero'* dose estimates
	1994–1996	All years	
Industrial radiography	34	577 (64%)	372
Major nuclear organisations	4	146 (16%)	87
Research, education and health institutions	16	181 (20%)	120
TOTAL	54	904	579 (64%)

* < 100 mGy.

TABLE 3 Comparative distribution of dose estimates obtained by physical and biological dosimetry

Method of dosimetry	Total number of estimates*					No physical or biological estimate possible
	Dose range (Sv or Gy)					
	0–0.09	0.1–0.29	0.3–0.99	1–9.99	10+	
Physical, eg by film or thermoluminescence dosemeter	260 (6)	123 (11)	121 (9)	85 (4)	35 (0)	280 (24)
Chromosomal aberrations	650 (38)	182 (16)	15 (0)	3 (0)	0 (0)	54 (0)

*1994–1996 figures are given in parentheses.

APPENDIX

Summary of Individual Cases Investigated in 1994–1996

A Possible non-uniform exposure in which the relationship between dose to the personal dosemeter and to the body is uncertain

A437

Cells scored	1000
Dicentrics	4
Centric rings	0
Other aberrations	5
Biological dose (Gy)	0.1
Thermoluminescence dosemeter (Sv)	body 0.41
	skin 0.26

An industrial radiographer was exposed when he worked close to a 250 kV x-ray set for 10–15 min. He wore no audible alarm and had relied upon a timer to switch off the set. However, the timer switch was faulty and when he returned to the control console he discovered that the tube was still activated. His thermoluminescence dosemeter worn on the chest had probably received a higher dose than the average to his whole body as he had leaned over the x-ray source.

A438

Cells scored	500
Dicentrics	1
Centric rings	0
Other aberrations	2
Biological dose (Gy)	0.1
Electronic dosemeter (Sv)	0.003
Film badge dose (Sv)	0.002

A 3.7 TBq (100 Ci) iridium-192 source fell out of its container and was swiftly grabbed by a worker and flung into a shielded bin. Had he held the source by its 'hot' end a hand dose of > 10 Gy was possible. No erythema developed and microwave thermography of the hand showed a normal picture. It appears therefore that, fortunately, he had held the source by its depleted uranium end and the likely hand dose was < 1 Gy. Chest-worn dosemeters and the chromosomal analysis reassured him that the general body dose was small.

5

A439

	(i)	(ii)
Cells scored	500	500
Dicentrics	1	3
Centric rings	0	1
Other aberrations	4	9
Biological doses (Gy)	0.1	see note
Film badge doses (Sv)	2.57	0.62

Two hospital technicians returned overdosed monthly badges. They worked with a variety of x- and γ-ray sources and during the month had carried out one non-routine procedure; a minor repair to a cobalt-60 unit. Person (i) was present in the room for about four times the period spent by person (ii) and shortly afterwards fell ill with 'flu'. This coincidence of events alarmed investigators although they could find no explanation for the badges being overexposed. The chromosomal analysis showed that clearly such doses had not been received and the aberrations seen in person (ii) were consistent with recent radiotherapy to a leg and shoulder for an arthritic condition.

A440

Cells scored	500
Dicentrics	1
Centric rings	0
Other aberrations	0
Biological dose (Gy)	0.1
Thermoluminescence dosemeter (Sv)	body 0.27

It was accepted that the dosemeter was irradiated when a hospital physicist accidentally left his badge pinned to a coat inside a linear accelerator room.

A441

Despite an initial explanation of a non-radiological cause for burns on both hands the clinical course of rapid necrotic ulceration was suspiciously like that which occurs after a very large radiation exposure (≥ 30 Gy acute). At a disciplinary hearing an account of an incident was eventually given in which a number of safety measures were flouted and the hands placed for about 20 s in an unfiltered beam from a 150 kV x-ray set.

Cells scored	500
Dicentrics	2
Centric rings	1
Other aberrations	3
Biological dose (Gy)	0.1
Thermoluminescence dosemeter (Sv)	body 0 skin 0

A442

No explanation could be found for the overexposure recorded on a badge worn by a dentist. He worked with three x-ray sets at about 70 kV. All were in good order. The badge of a colleague was unexposed.

Cells scored	500
Dicentrics	0
Centric rings	0
Other aberrations	1
Biological dose (Gy)	0
Thermoluminescence dosemeter (Sv)	body 0.6

A443

Cells scored	500
Dicentrics	0
Centric rings	0
Other aberrations	1
Biological dose (Gy)	0
Thermoluminescence dosemeter (Sv)	body 0.45 skin 0.30

Exposure was presumed to be from a non-destructive testing γ-ray source. An incident had occurred during the issue period but when investigated it could only have resulted in personal doses of about 5 mSv. This accorded with 6 mSv registered on the badge of another person present. The high dose on the thermoluminescence dosemeter was therefore inexplicable.

A444

Cells scored	500
Dicentrics	0
Centric rings	0
Other aberrations	2
Biological dose (Gy)	0
Thermoluminescence dosemeter (Sv)	body 0.40 skin 1.13

A careful and meticulous radiographer usually worked at a fully interlocked x-ray compound. However, on occasion, he also worked off-site with cobalt-60 and iridium-192 sources. At these times he was double badged and the other dosemeters recorded no exposure. No explanation for the dose indicated by his thermoluminescence dosemeter was found and the chromosomal analysis supported the view that he had not been irradiated.

A445

Cells scored	500
Dicentrics	0
Centric rings	0
Other aberrations	1
Biological dose (Gy)	0
Thermoluminescence dosemeter (Sv)	body 0.02 skin 0.02

Although the recorded dose was below the detection limit for cytogenetics, the analysis was undertaken for reassurance in case many other exposures had occurred and not been recorded on the badge. It was discovered that a new x-ray set had been installed in a compound but had not been connected to the door interlock. Safety depended on the radiographer remembering to shut the door and a dose of 20 mSv was consistent with a single occasion when the door was left ajar.

A446

Cells scored	500
Dicentrics	1
Centric rings	0
Other aberrations	1
Biological dose (Gy)	0.1
Thermoluminescence dosemeter (Sv)	body 0.08 skin 0.10

There was no apparent reason for this overexposure. The man used a pneumatic γ source in a properly interlocked cell. There had been a fault reported but the man was adamant that he had always entered the cell carrying a audible radiation alarm. The view was nevertheless taken that a genuine exposure had occurred.

9

A447

A film badge was irradiated out of its holder but the image had a sharp edge as if the film had been partly shielded. No explanation was found. The wearer of the badge was a conscientious hospital technician with access to a wide range of x-ray sets and γ sources.

Cells scored	500
Dicentrics	0
Centric rings	0
Other aberrations	0
Biological dose (Gy)	0
Film badge dose (Sv)	0.24

A448

This badge had been issued to a worker at a 'megacuries' cobalt-60 sterilisation plant. He was in good health and the few aberrations seen could probably be explained by his occupational exposure for many years within permitted limits.

Cells scored	500
Dicentrics	2
Centric rings	0
Other aberrations	1
Biological dose (Gy)	0.15
Thermoluminescence dosemeter (Sv)	body 2.60 skin 9.65

10

A449

An exposure occurred when a young operating-theatre nurse was working with a 60 kV fluoroscopy x-ray set which he mistakenly assumed to be switched off. His badge was probably in the full unattenuated beam and overrepresented the average dose to his body.

Cells scored	500
Dicentrics	0
Centric rings	0
Other aberrations	3
Biological dose (Gy)	0
Film badge dose (Sv)	0.12

A450

It was claimed that the dosemeter issued to a night-shift worker had been exposed deliberately to cause trouble. However, investigators found that the ceiling to a radiation compound had been damaged and suspected that the worker entered the area by this route and so bypassed interlocks. An overexposure was supported by the chromosomal findings.

Cells scored	500
Dicentrics	4
Centric rings	0
Other aberrations	14
Biological dose (Gy)	0.25
Thermoluminescence dosemeter (Sv)	body 0.14 skin 0.21

A451

A worker developed stress-related illness, probably caused by worry that he had been seriously irradiated whilst working abroad. He was employed by an unlicensed company to use unfamiliar radiographic equipment in a workplace where general safety standards were very lax. No training, written instructions, radiation monitors or personal dosemeters were provided. He privately obtained an outdated thermoluminescence dosemeter which he wore for about 1 year. The chromosomal analysis seemed to provide some reassurance that he had not been highly overexposed.

Cells scored	500
Dicentrics	1
Centric rings	0
Other aberrations	2
Biological dose (Gy)	0.1
Thermoluminescence dosemeter (Sv)	body 0.22
	skin 0.18

A452

A colleague pulled a worker out of an x-ray room when he realised that she was setting up metal objects for radiography with the set switched on due to a faulty interlock. A dose of 0.25–1.5 Sv was thought possible but because of the narrowness of the beam it would have been confined to her head and shoulders as she bent over the front of the tube. Her thermoluminescence dosemeter was worn at the waist. The part body nature of the exposure was possibly supported by the observation of two of the dicentrics being in the same cell.

Cells scored	500
Dicentrics	3
Centric rings	1
Other aberrations	2
Biological dose (Gy)	0.15
Thermoluminescence dosemeter (Sv)	body 0
	skin 0

12

A453

A clinical radiographer who worked with a linear accelerator returned an exposed badge. She also wore a finger-tip thermoluminescence dosemeter which was unexposed. Badges of colleagues in the same work area were also clear. No reason could be found for the high recorded dose.

Cells scored	500
Dicentrics	0
Centric rings	0
Other aberrations	1
Biological dose (Gy)	0
Film badge dose (Sv)	0.09

A454

Two successive monthly badges issued to a dental nurse were returned overexposed. The x-ray sets of the practice were in good working order. The nurse was sure that she had not been exposed and indeed, because she was pregnant, she had been doing far less radiography than usual. It was suspected that the films had been deliberately placed in an x-ray beam.

Cells scored	500
Dicentrics	0
Centric rings	0
Other aberrations	1
Biological dose (Gy)	0
Film badge doses (Sv)	0.1 and 0.03

13

A455

The dose was recorded on a finger-tip thermoluminescence dosemeter worn by a researcher using phosphorus-32. It was concluded that the exposure was confined to the hand and had probably resulted from a contaminated glove worn for about 20 min.

Cells scored	500
Dicentrics	0
Centric rings	0
Other aberrations	0
Biological dose (Gy)	0
Thermoluminescence dosemeter (Sv)	1.9

A456

It was suggested that the dosemeter had been inadvertently passed through an x-ray security device. The unclassified wearer worked with a sealed and well-shielded americium-241 source from which it should not have been possible to receive such a dose.

Cells scored	500
Dicentrics	1
Centric rings	0
Other aberrations	0
Biological dose (Gy)	0.05
Film badge dose (Sv)	0.14

A457

This was a quite unexpected badge reading. The worker was clearly in good health and investigators accepted his explanation that he had probably left the dosemeter close to some industrial radiographic equipment.

Cells scored	500
Dicentrics	1
Centric rings	0
Other aberrations	1
Biological dose (Gy)	0.1
Thermoluminescence dosemeter (Sv)	body 1.44 skin 1.94

A458

It was concluded that this badge had been accidentally mislaid. It was found beneath the hood of an x-ray cabinet used for routine inspections in the manufacture of car tyres.

Cells scored	500
Dicentrics	0
Centric rings	0
Other aberrations	2
Biological dose (Gy)	0
Thermoluminescence dosemeter (Sv)	body 0.41 skin 0.29

15

A459

Automatic winding gear for manoeuvering a cobalt-60 source in and out of its shielded position was defective, but it was still possible to use a manual system. This was done but the manual winding mechanism did not connect with some safety systems such as warning lights. Safety was dependent on the operator remembering to enter the cell carrying a dose-rate meter. Investigators concluded that he did not do this and on one occasion he had remained in the cell for about 5 min with the source partly jutting out from its safe housing.

Cells scored	500
Dicentrics	2
Centric rings	0
Other aberrations	0
Biological dose (Gy)	0.15
Thermoluminescence dosemeter (Sv)	body 0.19 skin 0.17

A460

This badge was issued to an administrator who did not work with radiation. It was kept on his desk and there was no explanation for its high exposure. Years previously, the man had been a classified worker and the company had failed to cancel his dosemeters when he ceased to do that work.

Cells scored	500
Dicentrics	0
Centric rings	0
Other aberrations	2
Biological dose (Gy)	0
Thermoluminescence dosemeter (Sv)	body 0.54 skin 3.11

16

UNIVERSITY OF HERTFORDSHIRE LRC

A461

	(i)	(ii)
Cells scored	1000	500
Dicentrics	3	0
Centric rings	0	0
Other aberrations	7	0
Biological doses (Gy)	see note	0
Film badge doses (Sv)	0.25	0.28

The men worked in the construction industry with nuclear density gauges that contain americium-241/beryllium and caesium-137. However, due to bad weather the sources were not used for the entire month when the badges recorded overdoses. The men were of the opinion that the badges had been irradiated at some point in a multi-step route from the dosimetry laboratory to their workplace. However no obvious source could be identified. The aberrations in person (i) were consistent with extensive diagnostic radiology a few months previously and therefore the absence of chromosomal damage in his colleague was taken to indicate that neither had been occupationally exposed.

A462

Cells scored	1000
Dicentrics	4
Centric rings	1
Other aberrations	3
Biological dose (Gy)	0.15
Thermoluminescence dosemeter (Sv)	body 0.32

A radiographer routinely worked with iridium-192 sources for examining aircraft engines. No incident occurred and no explanation could be found for the overdosed badge. However, the aberration yield was above background and as he had no previous medical or recorded occupational exposures it was concluded that he had been irradiated.

A463

Investigators accepted that the badge had been accidentally left in a radiation area by a worker at a γ sterilisation plant.

Cells scored	500
Dicentrics	0
Centric rings	0
Other aberrations	0
Biological dose (Gy)	0
Film badge dose (Sv)	0.3

A464

For most of the issue period the worker was absent on holiday and his dosemeter was left in a general mess-room attached to his work clothing. He attended work for 8 days but did not participate in any radiography. No one could account for the irradiation of the badge.

Cells scored	500
Dicentrics	0
Centric rings	0
Other aberrations	0
Biological dose (Gy)	0
Thermoluminescence dosemeter (Sv)	body 0.19 skin 0.22

B Suspected overexposure of persons not wearing a dosemeter

B106

Cells scored	500
Dicentrics	1
Centric rings	0
Other aberrations	2
Biological dose (Gy)	0.1

A worker feared that he had been irradiated when he suffered a patch of swollen red skin. The medical opinion was that it was a bacterial infection and it responded to antibiotics. The man's worry centred on an 'incident' when visiting a nuclear site and a fuel flask was unexpectedly manoeuvred close to him. He had forgotten to wear his personal dosemeter. The site records indicated that at the time the flask had been empty. He had worked in the nuclear industry for over 20 years, typically recording around 15 mSv y^{-1}, and the few aberrations seen were thought to be consistent with this. However, in addition, one very heavily damaged cell was found; see discussion in main text.

B107

Cells scored	500
Dicentrics	1
Centric rings	0
Other aberrations	0
Biological dose (Gy)	0.1

This person feared that she had been exposed to a very radioactive mineral specimen offered for sale. She claimed that it emitted dose rates of 'sieverts per hour' and suggested that it was a piece of solidified Chernobyl fuel. The item was, unfortunately, no longer available for inspection. The chromosomal analysis did not support her fears.

B108

A man developed a neurosis from an irrational belief that he had been seriously irradiated. A few hours after having his ankles x-rayed he developed painful testicles and rigour. He could not accept a medical opinion that this was a coincidental infection. He was convinced that he had been rendered sterile by the x rays.

Cells scored	500
Dicentrics	0
Centric rings	0
Other aberrations	0
Biological dose (Gy)	0

B109

These men were involved in a confusing situation when an emergency evacuation of a building required them to pass through a radiography area. Chromosomes from man (i) were examined first and aberrations found. This prompted the others to be sampled but nothing significant was found. Scoring was continued to 2500 cells in man (i) to improve the statistics. Although he had no recollection of exposures, for example for medical reasons, it was concluded that he had been exposed previously and that no radiation was received in the evacuation.

	(i)	(ii)	(iii)	(iv)	(v)	(vi)
Cells scored	2500	500	500	500	500	500
Dicentrics	6	0	0	1	0	0
Centric rings	0	0	0	0	0	0
Other aberrations	14	1	2	3	2	0
Biological doses (Gy)	0.05	0	0	0.05	0	0

B110

These men worked approximately 8 m from a position where weld radiography was repeatedly undertaken with a 600 GBq (16 Ci) iridium-192 source. The contract radiographers insisted that there was only one occasion when the men might have been exposed and if so the doses were, at worse, about 1 mSv. However, concern was increased when it was found that a stock of films stored about 100 m from the radiography point was fogged.

B110	(i)	(ii)	(iii)	(iv)
Cells scored	500	500	500	500
Dicentrics	0	0	0	1
Centric rings	0	0	0	0
Other aberrations	0	0	2	1
Biological doses (Gy)	0	0	0	0.1

B111

An exposure of 1 min to an industrial 200 kV x-ray set was feared and, if true, it was calculated that the likely dose would be < 1 mSv. The chromosomal analysis was undertaken because of the extreme anxiety of a non-radiation worker. Later, it was asserted by a contract radiographer that the set had been switched off at the time of the supposed incident.

B111	
Cells scored	500
Dicentrics	0
Centric rings	0
Other aberrations	0
Biological dose (Gy)	0

B112

A patient was given a technicium-99m labelled compound for a diagnostic bone scan, entailing an estimated equivalent dose of about 4 mSv. A family member asserted that a much higher dose had been administered. This claim was based on a measurement made by holding a Geiger–Müller tube to her body. The chromosomal analysis did not support this assertion.

Cells scored	500
Dicentrics	1
Centric rings	0
Other aberrations	1
Biological dose (Gy)	0.05

B113

A scientist reported an erythema which he believed was due to radiation. The medical opinion was that it was due to an insect sting. Chromosomal analysis showed aberrations not significantly different from background.

Cells scored	500
Dicentrics	1
Centric rings	0
Other aberrations	3
Biological dose (Gy)	0.1

B114

A maintenance worker bypassed a door interlock to enter a linear accelerator, mistakenly thinking that he had switched off the machine. When inside, he switched on an installed monitor which indicated radiation and automatically operated an emergency shutdown procedure. Until the shutdown he had moved in and out of a narrow beam for about 3 min. A 'worst case' calculation of average body dose was 10 mSv.

Cells scored	500
Dicentrics	0
Centric rings	0
Other aberrations	1
Biological dose (Gy)	0

B115

A nuclear medicine technician dropped a therapy ampoule of iodine-131 on the floor; fortunately it did not break. She left the room promptly to consider what to do next. She then re-entered, retrieved the source and placed it in a shielded pot. Despite advice that her γ-ray exposure would have been minimal she was very worried, and chromosomal analysis was carried out for reassurance.

Cells scored	500
Dicentrics	0
Centric rings	0
Other aberrations	1
Biological dose (Gy)	0

23

D Chronic internal or external exposure

D78

An inhalation and/or skin uptake of tritium was feared for a person who worked over a few days with 'curie quantities' of tritium labelled organic compounds in a fume cupboard.

Cells scored	500
Dicentrics	0
Centric rings	0
Other aberrations	0
Biological dose (Gy)	0

D79

A man who had worked, unmonitored, for several years with γ sources and more recently with a security x-ray set was found at a routine medical examination to be lymphopenic and thrombocytopenic. No particular cause could be found and his medical advisor was anxious to exclude the possibility of radiation.

Cells scored	500
Dicentrics	0
Centric rings	1
Other aberrations	2
Biological dose (Gy)	0

D80

A routine health and safety inspection of a laboratory revealed that phosphorus-32 had been used for the past 3 years by a researcher without permission and without the knowledge of the rest of the staff. Contamination of several items of equipment was found. Four persons who used the room regularly were referred for medical examinations. All were apparently healthy and chromosomally normal.

	(i)	(ii)	(iii)	(iv)
Cells scored	500	500	500	500
Dicentrics	0	0	0	0
Centric rings	0	0	0	0
Other aberrations	2	2	1	1
Biological doses (Gy)	0	0	0	0